P9-CPV-255

A New Day

Grateful acknowledgment is made to the following publishers, authors, and agents for their permission to reprint copyrighted material. Any adaptations are noted in the individual acknowledgments and are made with the full knowledge and approval of the authors or their representatives. Every effort has been made to locate all copyright proprietors; any errors or omissions in copyright notice are inadvertent and will be corrected in future printings as they are discovered.

"Alanike and the Storyteller" by Donita Creola, © 1989 by Silver, Burdett & Ginn Inc.

"All of Our Noses Are Here" adapted from *All of Our Noses Are Here and Other Noodle Tales.* Retold by Alvin Schwartz. Pictures by Karen Ann Weinhaus. Text copyright © 1985 by Alvin Schwartz. Illustrations copyright © 1985 by Karen Ann Weinhaus. Reprinted by permission of Harper & Row, Publishers, Inc., and of the author's agents, Curtis Brown Ltd.

"Alone" excerpt adapted from *Days with Frog and Toad* by Arnold Lobel. Text and art copyright © 1979 by Arnold Lobel. Reprinted with permission of the American publishers, Harper and Row, Publishers, Inc., and of the British publishers, William Heinemann Ltd.

"City" from *The Langston Hughes Reader* by Langston Hughes. Reprinted by permission of Harold Ober Associates Incorporated. Copyright © 1958 by Langston Hughes. Copyright renewed 1986 by George Houston Bass.

Dreams written and illustrated by Ezra Jack Keats, reprinted by permission of Macmillan Publishing Company. Copyright © 1974 Ezra Jack Keats.

"Goldfish and Lee" by Mitchell Sharmat, © 1989 by Silver, Burdett & Ginn Inc.

"Lee Bennett Hopkins Interviews Jerry Pinkney," © 1989 by Silver, Burdett & Ginn Inc.

"The Man, the Cat, and the Sky" by Barbara Juster Esbensen, © 1989 by Silver, Burdett & Ginn Inc.

The Midnight Farm by Reeve Lindbergh, paintings by Susan Jeffers. Text copyright © 1987 by Reeve Lindbergh. Pictures copyright © 1987 by Susan Jeffers. Excerpt reprinted by permission of the Dial Books for Young Readers, and of the artist's attorney, Sheldon Fogelman.

"A New Day in the City" by Alice Benjamin Boynton, © 1989 by Silver, Burdett & Ginn Inc.

"Once Upon a Time" by Neil Davis, © 1989 by Silver, Burdett & Ginn Inc.

"Since Hanna Moved Away" from *If I Were in Charge of the World and Other Worries* by Judith Viorst. Copyright © 1981 Judith Viorst. Reprinted with the permission of the American publisher, Atheneum Publishers, an imprint of Macmillan Publishing Company, the author's American agents, Lescher & Lescher, Ltd., and of the author's British agents A. M. Heath & Company Ltd.

"Some Fun" written and illustrated by James Marshall, © 1989 by Silver, Burdett & Ginn Inc.

"Stone Soup" adapted by Marjorie and Mitchell Sharmat, © 1989 by Silver, Burdett & Ginn Inc.

Acknowledgments continue on page 256, which constitutes an extension of this copyright page.

 ISBN 0-663-46113-8

A NEW DAY

P. DAVID PEARSON   DALE D. JOHNSON

THEODORE CLYMER   ROSELMINA INDRISANO   RICHARD L. VENEZKY

JAMES F. BAUMANN   ELFRIEDA HIEBERT   MARIAN TOTH

Consulting Authors

CARL GRANT   JEANNE PARATORE

SILVER BURDETT & GINN

NEEDHAM, MA • MORRISTOWN, NJ

ATLANTA, GA • CINCINNATI, OH • DALLAS, TX

MENLO PARK, CA • NORTHFIELD, IL

FRIENDS FOREVER

UNIT ONE

STORYTELLERS

UNIT TWO

DIGGING ON THE SANDS.

UNIT ONE

FRIENDS FOREVER

We meet friends in school. We meet friends in books.

What makes a friend a friend?

DIGGING ON THE SANDS,
ceramic tiles c. 1900

YOUR FRIEND, LITTLE BEAR

from *Little Bear's Friend*

written by Else Holmelund Minarik
illustrated by Maurice Sendak

Summer is over, and Little Bear's friend must go back to school. Little Bear finds a way to stay friends.

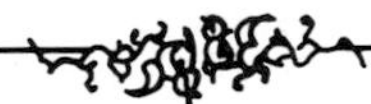

Summer was over,
and Emily was saying goodbye.
It was time to go
back to school.
Mother Bear baked a cake.
Little Bear made lemonade.

Mother Bear said,
"Let us eat up all the cake.
If we do, then it will not
rain tomorrow."

"Let it rain," said Little Bear.
"Emily will not be here tomorrow
to play with me."

So they ate the cake,
and drank the lemonade,
and talked and talked.

They talked until it was time
for Emily to go home.

Emily opened her pocketbook.
She took out a fine new pen.
"This is for you," she said.
"I want you to have it."

Little Bear took the pen.
"Thank you, Emily," he said.

He ran into his room,
and came back with a toy boat.

"This is for you," he said.
"For keeps.
You can sail it in your bathtub."

"Thank you," said Emily. "I will.
Goodbye, Little Bear.
See you next summer."

Little Bear stood at the door.
Two big tears ran down his face.

Mother Bear saw them,
and took him on her lap.

"My goodness, Little Bear," she said.
"You will be going to school, too,
and you will learn to write.
Then you can write to Emily."

And soon he did write to Emily,
like this:

Dear Emily,

It is snowing.
I love the snow.
I wish I could send you some.
Owl, Duck, Hen, and Cat
send their love.
So do the ducklings.
I cannot wait for summer.

Your friend,
Little Bear

Reader's Response

Do you think that Emily's gift was a good gift for Little Bear? Tell why or why not.

SELECTION FOLLOW-UP

YOUR FRIEND, LITTLE BEAR

Questions

1. Why was Emily going away?
2. Why did Little Bear give Emily a boat?
3. Was Little Bear sad to see Emily go? How do you know?
4. Tell what happened first, next, and last in the story.

Writing to Learn

THINK AND PRETEND You are Emily. You write a letter back to Little Bear. What would you say?

Dear Little Bear,
I liked your letter. I miss you and Owl, Duck, Cat, and Hen. I miss the ducklings, too.
Your friend,
Emily

WRITE On a piece of paper, write what you think Emily would say to Little Bear.

two friends

lydia and shirley have
two pierced ears and
two bare ones
five pigtails
two pairs of sneakers
two berets
two smiles
one necklace
one bracelet
lots of stripes and
one good friendship

Nikki Giovanni

A Strategy for Thinking:

Drawing Story Pictures

You can draw a picture about a story. Here is a picture someone drew about "Your Friend, Little Bear."

What is happening in the picture?

Read the poem "Our Mr. Toad" by David McCord. Draw a picture about the poem.

Our Mr. Toad
Has a nice abode
Under the first front step.
When it rains he's cool
In a secret pool
Where the water goes
  drip
  drop
  drep.

What did you put in your picture?

Read the next story. Some questions will ask you to draw a picture. Try to answer the questions.

The writing connection can be found on page 59.

Frog and Toad learn something new about being best friends.

Alone

from *Days with Frog and Toad*

written and illustrated
by Arnold Lobel

Toad went to Frog's house.
There was a note on the door.
The note said,
"Dear Toad, I am not at home.
I went out.
I want to be alone."

"Alone?" said Toad.

"Frog has me for a friend.

Why does he want to be alone?"

Toad went to the woods.

Frog was not there.

He went to the meadow.

Frog was not there.

Toad went down to the river.

There was Frog.

He was sitting on an island

by himself.

"Poor Frog," said Toad.
"He must be very sad.
I will cheer him up."
Toad ran home.
He made sandwiches.
He made tea.
He put everything
in a basket.

What picture would you draw about Toad?

Then Toad ran back to the river.

"Frog," he called, "it's me.

It's your best friend, Toad!"

Frog was too far away to hear.

Toad jumped up and down.

Frog was too far away to see.

A turtle swam by.

Toad got on the turtle's back.

"Turtle," said Toad,

"take me to the island.

Frog is there.

He wants to be alone."

What picture would you draw about Toad?

"If Frog wants to be alone,"
said the turtle,
"why don't you leave him alone?"
"Maybe you are right," said Toad.
"Maybe Frog does not
want to see me.
Maybe he does not want me
to be his friend anymore."
"Yes, maybe," said the turtle
as he swam to the island.

"Frog!" called Toad.

"I am sorry for all
the silly things I do.
I am sorry for all
the silly things I say.
Please be my friend again!"
Toad slipped off the turtle.
He fell in the river.

What picture would you draw about Toad?

Frog pulled Toad
up onto the island.
Toad looked in the basket.
The sandwiches were wet.
There was no more tea.
"Our lunch is wet," said Toad.
"I made it for you, Frog,
so that you would be happy."
"But Toad," said Frog.
"I AM happy. I am very happy.

This morning
when I woke up
I felt good because
the sun was out.
I felt good because
I was a frog.
And I felt good because
I have you for a friend." ◆◆◆

◆◆◆
What picture would you draw about Frog and Toad?

Frog and Toad
stayed on the island all day.
They ate wet sandwiches
without tea.
They were two best friends
sitting alone together.

Draw a picture about this story. Write or tell about your picture.

◆ LIBRARY LINK ◆

"Alone" came from a book called Days with Frog and Toad. *Look for it and other Frog and Toad books in your library.*

Reader's Response

Do you think Toad was a good friend to Frog? Tell why or why not.

Selection Follow-Up

Alone

Questions

1. Why did Toad think that Frog was sad?
2. What is one thing Toad did to try to cheer up Frog?
3. Frog wanted to be alone. How do you know this?

Writing to Learn

Think and Pretend Frog left a note on his door for Toad. It said that Frog wanted to be alone. If you left a note for Toad, what would you write?

Dear Toad,
I am at the park.
I want to be alone.
Your friend,
Mike

Write On your paper write a note to Toad.

Frogs in Stories

You have just read a story about a frog. Here are some famous frogs from other stories. Each artist draws frogs differently. Look at the pictures. Can you tell something different about each frog?

What things can you tell about this frog? . . .

Or this frog? . . .

Or this frog?

Which frog would you have the most fun with?

You will meet another frog in this unit. Here is what he looks like.

A New Day in the City

by Alice Benjamin Boynton

In this story, Benita finds a way to cheer up a sick friend.

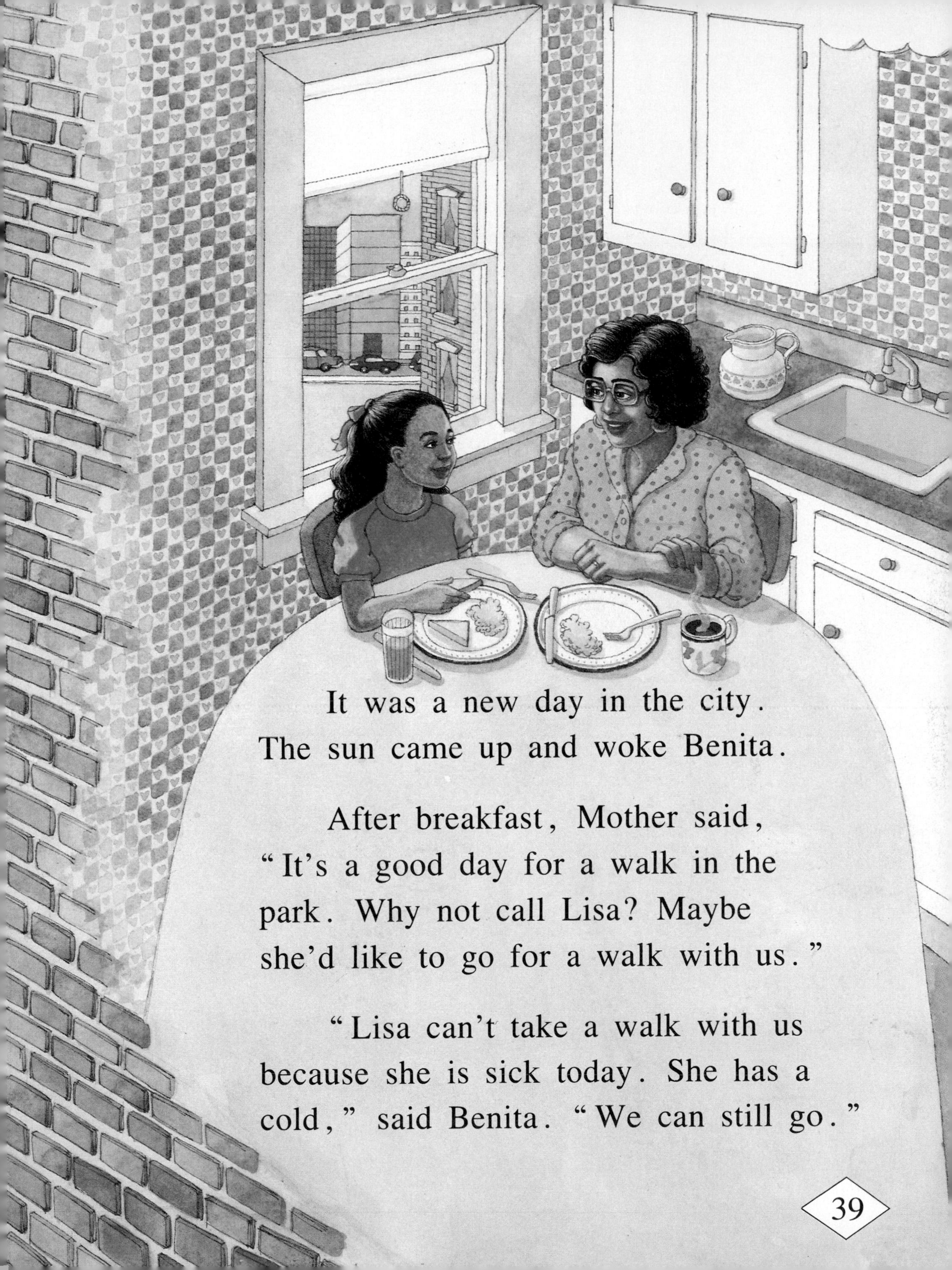

It was a new day in the city. The sun came up and woke Benita.

After breakfast, Mother said, "It's a good day for a walk in the park. Why not call Lisa? Maybe she'd like to go for a walk with us."

"Lisa can't take a walk with us because she is sick today. She has a cold," said Benita. "We can still go."

So Mother and Benita walked to the park. On the way, they saw Mr. Green's dog, Missy. Missy sat in a box by Mr. Green's chair. She licked Benita's hand.

"She must want to tell us something," Benita said to Mother. "I wish she could talk."

When they came to the duck pond in the park, the big white duck quacked and quacked.

"What is it, duck?" Benita asked. "I wish you could talk."

Then Mother said, "Benita, look up!"

In the big tree sat the mother bird and her three little birds. The mother bird sang to Benita.

"She'd like to tell me something, too," said Benita. "What could it be? I wish she could talk."

The next day, Lisa was still sick. After breakfast, Benita and Mother went for a walk in the park.

Mr. Green called to Benita. "Benita," he said. "Come and see what Missy has to show you."

Missy was still in the box. But now there were three little tan puppies in the box, too.

"That's what she wanted to tell you," said Mother.

When they got to the park, Mother and Benita looked for the big white duck. There she was with three little ducks.

"Quack, quack, quack!" said the mother duck.

"Oh," Benita laughed. "That's what you wanted to tell me. I'm sorry Lisa isn't here to meet your ducklings."

Next, Benita looked for the little birds in the nest. Benita saw them flying away from the tree.

"Look, Mother," cried Benita. "The little birds can fly!"

"That must be what the mother bird wanted to tell us," said Mother.

"There are lots of surprises in the city," said Benita. "I'll be glad when Lisa is well again. I know she'd like to see them, too. Wait! I know a way to show her everything I saw."

When Benita got home, she ran to get some paints and paper. She painted a picture of Missy and her puppies. She painted the duck family on the pond. She painted the little birds flying from the nest.

After Benita had painted the pictures, she called Lisa.

Benita said, "I'm sorry you weren't with us today. I miss you. You can't go for a walk with me today. But I can show you all the surprises Mother and I saw. Just wait and see!"

The next afternoon Benita and her mother took the pictures to Lisa's house. Together they put up the pictures in her room. The room looked just like the park. Lisa was so happy.

"I'm glad you're my friend, Benita," she said. "I can't wait to go for a walk with you. Then we can look for all the new things in the park."

Reader's Response

Do you think Benita found a good way to cheer up Lisa? Tell why or why not.

SELECTION FOLLOW-UP

A New Day in the City

Questions

1. What surprise did Missy have for Benita?
2. Name two ways in which Benita was a good friend to Lisa.
3. Where does Benita live? How do you know?

Writing to Learn

THINK AND DECIDE If you were Mr. Green, what would you name Missy's puppies? Draw a picture of Missy and her puppies.

WRITE Label Missy. Write the name you chose for each puppy on your picture.

CITY

by Langston Hughes

In the morning the city
Spreads its wings
Making a song
In stone that sings.

In the evening the city
Goes to bed
Hanging lights
About its head.

Together

by Anne Rockwell

Sometimes friends share what each can do well.

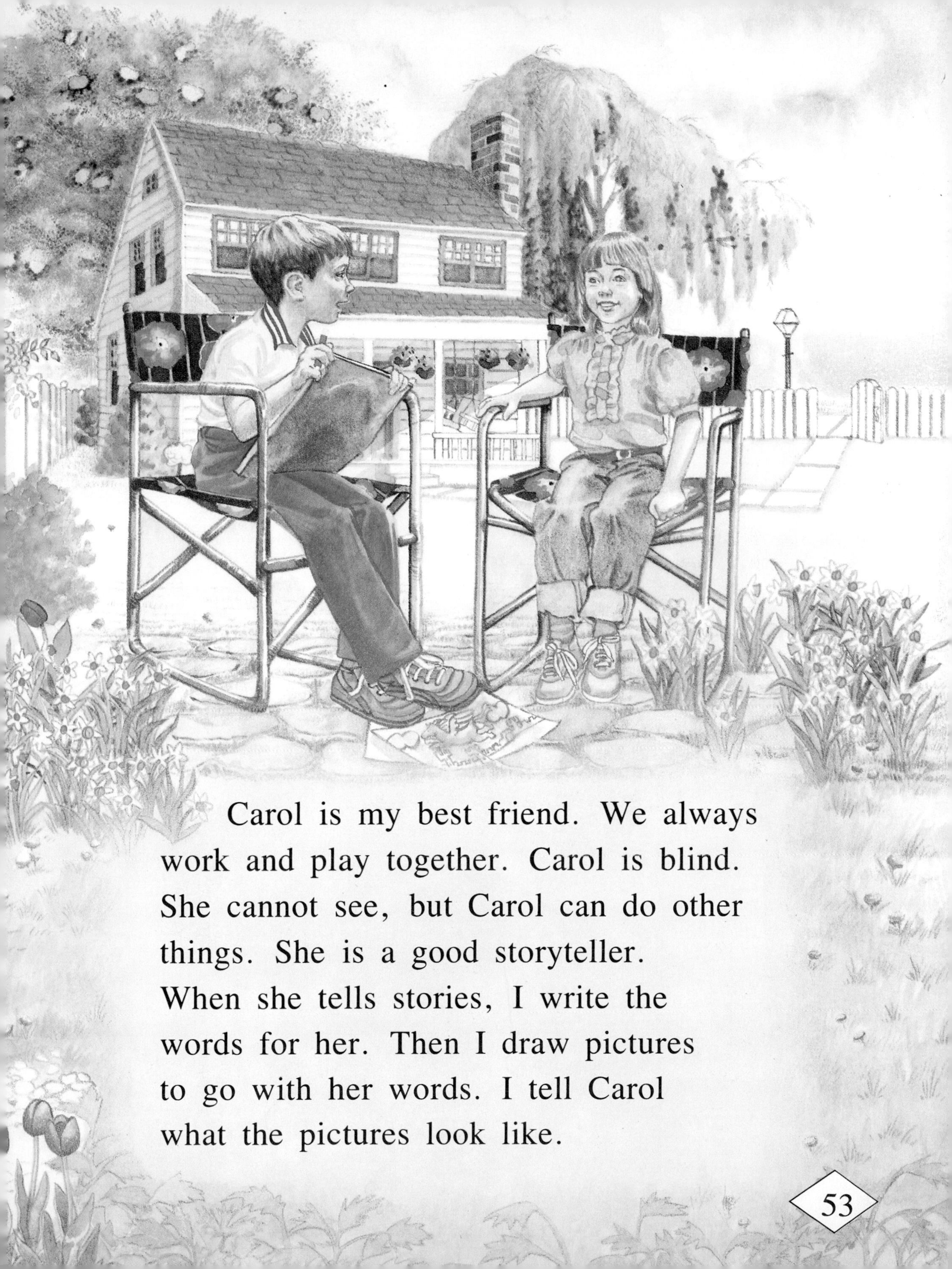

Carol is my best friend. We always work and play together. Carol is blind. She cannot see, but Carol can do other things. She is a good storyteller. When she tells stories, I write the words for her. Then I draw pictures to go with her words. I tell Carol what the pictures look like.

Carol can play the guitar. I love to hear her play. Sometimes I try to play the guitar, too. Carol helps me. First she shows me how to hold the guitar. Then she tells me to feel the strings as I play. We play and sing together.

Carol and I love to read together. I read with my eyes. Carol reads with her fingers. Her books are special. The words are made with dots. People who are blind feel the dots to read the words.

Carol shows me how she reads. I can feel the dots with my fingers. I try to read the dots, but I can't. Carol reads them for me.

Carol and I have our own garden. It is work to plant a garden. My dad helps. He finds seeds for us to plant.

First, we plant the seeds in the ground. Then we water them. My dad helps us put water in the watering can. Sometimes I can't hold the watering can. Carol and I do it together.

Then we wait for the first plants to come up. At last a little green plant pops up out of the ground. Carol and I run to tell my dad. I tell Carol about the plant and she feels it with her fingers. It is a special day for us.

Carol and I love to work and play together. We always have a lot of fun. We are glad that we can share so many special things.

Reader's Response

Would you like to have a friend like Carol? Tell why or why not.

SELECTION FOLLOW-UP

Together

Questions

1. How did Carol help her friend?
2. Why did Carol read with her fingers?
3. Carol liked her friend. What tells you this?
4. Tell the order in which Carol and her friend planted their garden.

Writing to Learn

THINK AND DRAW Friends share. What would you like to share with Carol if she were your friend? Draw a picture of you and Carol.

WRITE Write some words about Carol. Tell what you and Carol are doing.

Reading in a Content Area: Social Studies

Learning from Pictures

Words and pictures in your social studies book tell you about people and places. Pictures show you what people look like and where they live. They show you things people do. Sometimes they can show you how people feel.

What are the people doing in this picture?

Did you answer that people are feeding hay to the horse? Can you tell the time of year?

What is happening in the picture below?

Here are some clues. The door looks big, like a school door. The boy has a lunch box in his hand. Did you say that the boy is going to school?

As You Read Read the following pages from a social studies book. Answer the questions on page 65.

How do family members help one another?

Family members help each other.

They help each other work.
They help each other learn.

What are some days families celebrate?

Families **celebrate** special days.
Birthdays are special days.

Holidays are
special days.

Using What You Have Learned

1. You learn on page 62 that family members help one another. What are the family members doing to help one another?

2. Look at the picture of the father and the boy on page 63. What are the father and boy doing?

3. Look at the picture at the top of page 64. How do you think the grandfather feels?

4. What is happening in the picture at the bottom of page 64?

Examples and excerpts are from *Families and Their Needs, Silver Burdett & Ginn Social Studies,* © 1988.

Goldfish and Lee

by Mitchell Sharmat

When Lee visits Terry, he meets an unexpected friend.

This is a big day. Mom and I are going to visit my cousin, Terry. Terry lives on a farm. I live in the city with my mom. Sometimes Terry visits me in the city. Then I have to teach him how to do a lot of things. And Terry always has something new to teach me about the farm. Today he's going to show me how to ride his new horse!

Soon Mom and I are at Terry's farm. We see lots of people working. We see sheep, hens, and cows. But where is Terry's horse? I have never been close to a horse before, and I can't wait to ride it.

"Look over there, Lee," says Mom. "There's a horse near the barn. It looks golden in the sun. Terry's near the barn, too."

I start to run to Terry and the horse. But then I stop. The horse looks so big! When I get close to it, I feel as small as an ant.

Terry smiles when I tell him how small I feel. So I say, "Don't you feel small when you come to the city?"

"Well, yes," Terry says and smiles. "Sometimes I do."

Terry tries to help me.

"Talk to Goldfish," he says.

So I say, "Hello, Goldfish. My name is Lee. How are you?"

Goldfish shakes his head.

"That means hello," Terry says. "Now rub his nose."

So I reach out and rub Goldfish's nose. It feels as soft as fur.

By now I can tell that I'm going to like this horse.

"Do you want to ride him?" Terry asks.

"Sure," I say. Then I get on Goldfish, the horse.

"Hold on," says Terry. "I'm going to take you for a walk." He leads Goldfish across the grass.

"This is fun," I tell Terry.

Terry smiles. "I thought you'd like it," he says.

"Now watch this," Terry says. "You'll see why his name is Goldfish."

Terry leads Goldfish to the water. What do you think Goldfish does? He puts his nose under the water and blows into it!

"You see?" Terry laughs. "He thinks he's a fish!"

Too soon I have to say goodbye to Goldfish and Terry.

"That Goldfish is a neat horse," I tell Terry. "You can be sure I'll be back soon to ride him!"

Reader's Response

Would you like Terry to teach you how to do something? Tell why.

SELECTION FOLLOW-UP

Goldfish and Lee

Questions

1. Where did Lee live? Where did Terry live?
2. Why did Lee stop running when he got close to Goldfish?
3. How did Terry help Lee learn to ride a horse?
4. When Terry visits the city, what do you think Lee will show him? Why do you think this?

Writing to Learn

THINK AND DISCOVER Would you like to visit the farm where Terry lives? Think about what you would see and do there.

WRITE Write what you would see and do.

Since Hanna Moved Away

The tires on my bike are flat.
The sky is grouchy gray.
At least it sure feels like that
Since Hanna moved away.

Chocolate ice cream tastes like prunes.
December's come to stay.
They've taken back the Mays and Junes
Since Hanna moved away.

Flowers smell like halibut.
Velvet feels like hay.
Every handsome dog's a mutt
Since Hanna moved away.

Nothing's fun to laugh about.
Nothing's fun to play.
They call me, but I won't come out
Since Hanna moved away.

Judith Viorst

I miss you.
Love,
Hanna

We Are **BEST** Friends

written and illustrated by Aliki

READING TEACHER: CHILDREN'S CHOICE 1983

Robert and Peter find a way to stay friends even though Peter must move far away.

Peter came to tell Robert the news.
"I am moving away," he said.

"You can't move away," said Robert.
"We are best friends."

"I am moving far away," said Peter.
"We will live in a new house.
I will be going to a new school."

"What will you do without me?"
asked Robert.
"Who will you play with?
No one can play like best friends."

"I will make new friends," said Peter.

"You can't move away," said Robert.
"You will miss me too much."

But Peter moved away.
There was nothing to do without Peter.
There was no one to play with,
not the way best friends play.
There was no one to share with,
not the way best friends share.
There was no fun anymore.

"Hello. My name is Will,"
said a new face.
"I just moved here.
My friends are all at my old school."

"I don't like the name Will,"
thought Robert.

"My old school was fun," said Will,
"not like this place."

One day, a letter came for Robert.
It was a letter from Peter.

Dear Robert,
I like my new house now.
I like my new school now.
I didn't like anything when
I got here.

but now I have a friend, Alex.
You are my best friend,
But Alex is nice.
It is fun to have someone to play
with again.
Your best friend,
Peter

Robert drew Peter a letter.
He drew two friends playing
with their trucks.
He drew them on their bikes.
He wrote:

If you were here,
this is what we'd be doing.
But you're not.

Then he wrote:

There is a new boy in school.

Robert saw Will.
"Did you lose something?" he asked.

"I thought I saw a frog," said Will.

"That's funny, looking for a frog,"
said Robert.

"What's funny about it?
I like frogs," said Will.

"I know where there are frogs,"
said Robert.
"Right in my garden."

"You're just saying that," said Will.

"I mean it," said Robert.
"You can see for yourself."

"If I had a frog in my garden,
I would share it," said Will.

"That's what I'm doing," said Robert.

Robert and Will rode home together.
They went into the garden.
The frogs were there.
One jumped under a bush, and Will got it.
"You like me, don't you?"

"The frogs lay their eggs here each year," said Robert.
"My friend Peter used to come watch the tadpoles.
He'll miss them."

"Why?" asked Will.

"He moved away," said Robert.
"I write him letters."

"Then you can write about the tadpoles," said Will.

Robert wrote to Peter.

Dear Peter,
I can't wait until summer.
When you come to visit.
The new boy is called Will.
I showed him the frogs.
He had a pet one near his home,
but he had to move away, like you.

Love,
Robert

P.S. How is Alex ?
P.P.S. See you soon.

Robert mailed the letter,
then rode over to Will's house to play.

◆ LIBRARY LINK ◆

Look in the library for these books written and illustrated by Aliki: Digging Up Dinosaurs *and* Feelings.

Reader's Response

Do you think Robert and Peter will keep writing to each other? Tell why or why not.

SELECTION FOLLOW-UP

We Are **BEST** Friends

Questions

1. What news did Peter tell Robert in the beginning of the story?
2. When was Robert sad? What makes you think so?
3. What happened first in the story? What happened last?

Writing to Learn

THINK AND MAKE BELIEVE Make believe Peter is your friend. What would you say if you were writing to him?

WRITE Write a letter to Peter on your paper.

Literature:

Reality and Fantasy

Some stories are about real things. Some stories are about make-believe things. Sometimes the pictures in a story can help you decide whether a story is real or make-believe.

The picture above shows a real dog. What things tell you that the dog in the picture is real?

Using What You Have Learned

This is a picture of a dog you will meet in the next story, "Some Fun." Is this dog real or make-believe? What things helped you decide?

As You Read

The dog and the goldfish in the next story meet a shark. Look at the picture of the shark. Is it real or make-believe? How do you know?

Some Fun

written and illustrated
by James Marshall

Do friends have to like the same things? A dog and a goldfish like different things.

A dog and her goldfish were sitting by the fire.

"I want to have some fun," said the goldfish.

"But this is fun," said the dog.

"Not really," said the goldfish. "I want to go places and see things. I want to see the woods, the sky, and the sea. I want to see some sharks!"

"Oh, very well," said the dog.

"This is very kind of you," said the goldfish.

"Anything to keep you happy," said the dog. "But we can't go too far from home. We don't want to get lost."

"Where will we go first?" asked the goldfish.

"I know a place to see some sharks," said the dog. "It's not far."

"Oh, my!" cried the goldfish. "Sharks! Look at their teeth! This is really fun!"

"I'm glad you think so," said the dog. "Now can we go home?"

"Oh, no!" cried the goldfish. "I want to do more! Now I want to see the sea."

"Anything to keep you happy," said the dog.

"Look at the waves!" cried the goldfish. "This is really fun!"

But the dog did not like the sea. "The waves make me feel sick," she said. "Now can we go home?"

"Oh, no!" said the goldfish. "Now I want to see the sky. I want to fly."

"Anything to keep you happy," said the dog.

"This is really fun!" cried the goldfish. "Look at all the hills!"

But the dog did not like to fly. "I can't look down," she said. "I can't. Now can we go home?"

"Oh, no!" said the goldfish. "Before we go home, we must see the woods."

"Anything to keep you happy," said the dog.

"Oh, my!" cried the goldfish. "Look at all the trees."

The two friends looked all around the woods. Before long they were lost.

"I'm sorry," said the dog.
"I don't know how to get home."

"Are you lost?" asked a
kind elephant.

"Yes, we are," said the goldfish.

"Then I will take you home,"
said the elephant.

"This is very kind of you," said the dog.

"It is fun to go places and see things," said the elephant. "But it is good to go home, too."

"Yes, it is," said the dog.

Before long the dog and her goldfish were home.

"That was so much fun," said the goldfish. "Where will we go now?"

"Now we will sit at home by the fire," said the dog. "That is what I want to do."

"Anything to keep you happy," said the goldfish.

"You are very kind," said the dog.

Reader's Response

Why do you think the dog went with the goldfish when she really didn't want to?

Writing a Letter

You have read about friends. Friends like to get letters. You can write a letter to one of your friends.

Getting Ready

All letters have a beginning, a middle, and an end. Look at the letter below. Use it to help you plan your letter.

Dear (beginning) ________________,

____

(middle)
____

____

Your friend,

(end) ________________

Writing

Look at how this letter begins and ends. Begin your letter the same way. In the middle, write what you want to say to your friend. End your letter by writing your name.

Listening to My Writing

Read your letter aloud. Do you have any other news you want to tell your friend?

Sharing

Ask someone at home to help you write the envelope. Then put a stamp on it and mail it.

Making a Greeting Card

Terry lived far away from Lee. If Lee wanted to tell Terry something, he could send a greeting card.

Now you and a friend will work together to make a card. As you work, make sure you:

- ♦ Help each other think of ideas.
- ♦ Listen when the other person talks.

First gather the things you need to make a card. Then think of some classmates who would like to receive a card. Choose one person.

Think of some ideas for pictures to put on the card. You can each draw one picture on the card.

Will your card be a surprise?

May I Bring a Friend? by Beatrice Schenk de Regniers *(Atheneum, 1964)*. Each time a boy has tea with the King and Queen, he brings along a friend—an animal that causes many problems.

Friends by Helme Heine *(Atheneum, 1982)*. A pig, a rooster, and a mouse cannot fit into each other's houses. They agree that friends do not have to spend *every* moment together.

My Friend John by Charlotte Zolotow *(Harper & Row, 1968)*. Two young boys do things differently, but they are still best friends!

UNIT TWO

STORYTELLERS

What makes a story so special that you want to hear it over and over again?

PAINTED BOX,
Russian, contemporary

Once Upon a Time

by Neil Davis

Some stories can take you to make-believe places.

I like stories that begin "Once upon a time." "Once upon a time" stories take you to beautiful places that you can't visit.

I like " Once upon a time " stories. People can pretend to be as tall as a house or as small as a thumb. People can make soup from a stone or horses out of clouds. Sometimes people get three wishes. They can wish for anything they want.

I like "Once upon a time" stories because they are about animals that do pretend things. Pigs build houses, and bears sit in chairs. Small cats wear mittens, and hens bake bread.

I like " Once upon a time " stories because they are about pretend places. Kings and queens live in beautiful castles. Sometimes there is a beautiful princess in the castle.

I like stories that begin "Once upon a time." But what I like best about them is that they always end "happily ever after."

Reader's Response

What do you like best about "Once upon a time" stories?

SELECTION FOLLOW-UP

Once Upon a Time

Questions

1. What kind of stories was this article about? How do you know?
2. How are the people in "Once upon a time" stories different from you?
3. Why do you think most "Once upon a time" stories end "happily ever after"?

Writing to Learn

THINK AND IMAGINE Draw a picture of an animal or a person in a story you know.

WRITE On your paper, write "Once upon a time... ." Then tell one thing that happened to the animal or the person in your picture.

A Castle

banner
turret
moat

Study Skill:

Picture Dictionary

You can read the word drawbridge in "The Castle."

This picture shows part of a page from a Picture Dictionary.

Find the word drawbridge on the page.

A a

apple

An apple is to eat.

D d

drawbridge

The knights crossed over the drawbridge.

E e

egg

A hen lays an egg.

You can see that a Picture Dictionary lists words in ABC order.

In a Picture Dictionary, you will find a picture and a sentence for each word. The picture and the sentence help tell you what the word means.

Using What You Have Learned

Look at the Picture Dictionary again. Then answer these questions.

1. Why does drawbridge come before egg?
2. In your own words, tell what apple means.
3. What is a word that could come after egg?
4. Think of a word. Draw a picture of your word. Write a sentence that will tell others what your word means.
5. Where could you find the meaning of a word you didn't know?

The Man, the Cat, and the Sky

by Barbara Juster Esbensen

See how clouds help the man in this story.

Once upon a time there was a man. He had a big white cat called Cream. Their house and garden were by a river in the country. In the morning they would look at the green water. They would listen to the blue wind blow over the grass. The man would work in his garden. Cream would watch the colored fish swim by in the water.

One morning, the man was sad. Today the king and his friends would be playing games. The man wanted to go over the far hills to watch.

"I have never watched a king play games," he told Cream. "I would like to go, but I don't have a horse or even a tiny cart. How could we get there? It is too far for us to walk."

Cream looked sad. He wanted to see a king's cat. Maybe the king's cat played games, too.

The man stopped and looked up at the sky. It was as blue as could be. Then the man saw a big puff of white.

"I see a big ship up there, Cream!" he said. "Maybe that ship can take us to see the king. What do you think?"

Cream looked up. The ship was blowing away.

"Oh, no!" said the man. "We'll never get there! That ship can't take us to see the king's games."

The man turned to look at the sky again. "Now there are three white horses in the sky," he said. "Would you like to go with me to the king's town, Cream? We could race like the wind on the backs of these white horses. One horse is for you, one horse is for me. One horse will show us the way to go. What do you think, Cream?"

Cream looked up. The horses were blowing away.

"Oh, no!" said the man. "Now we can't go to see the king on the white horses!"

The man turned and looked up again. There was nothing to see this time. There was just the blue sky everywhere. "Now we will never see the king," he told Cream.

Cream did not hear the man's sad words. He was listening to something else. Cream could hear singing far up the river. Now the man listened, too.

It was the king! The king and his friends were singing and blowing their whistles. They came sailing down the river. Their little ship was filled with bright red tents.

The man said, "It is the king! Can this be true, Cream?"

Cream looked at the king and his black cat and the red tents. The wind did not blow them away.

The man sat down and took Cream on his lap. They watched the king and his friends play their games.

Reader's Response

Do you think what the man saw in the clouds was real? Tell why or why not.

SELECTION FOLLOW-UP

The Man, the Cat, and the Sky

Questions

1. Why was the man sad at the beginning of the story? How do you know this?
2. What did the man see in the sky?
3. Why did the things the man saw blow away?
4. Which of these story words would come first in the dictionary: *man, cat, sky, king, wind?* Why?

Writing to Learn

THINK AND LOOK When you look into the sky, what do you see? Look at this picture of the sky. What animals do you see?

WRITE Make a list of what you see in the picture.

In this story, three hungry people play a trick to get something to eat.

STONE SOUP

adapted by Marjorie and Mitchell Sharmat

Three travelers were on their way home. They walked through woods. They walked through meadows.

"I need to eat," said the first traveler.

"I need to sleep," said the second traveler.

"I need to eat and sleep," said the third traveler.

They kept walking down the road until they came to a little town.

The people in the town saw the three travelers coming down the road.

"They will want a place to eat and sleep," said one man. "What can we do?"

"Tell them the wolf ate all our food! Then we can hide it," said a second man.

"We can hide it under our beds," said a third.

The people ran to hide their food. Some people hid it under their beds. Some people hid their food in other places.

The three travelers came to the town.

"We have walked and walked," they said to the people. "May we have some food and a place to sleep?"

"A wolf ate all our food," said the people in the town.

"All we have is water," they said.

"Water!" the three travelers said. "Good! We can make stone soup with that."

"What is stone soup?" asked a woman.

"We'll show you," said the first traveler. "Find us a big pot. Then bring us some water and three, big flat stones. Then get us some sticks for a fire."

The people ran to get the pot, the water, and the sticks. Then they got the three, big, flat stones.

The travelers put the water and stones in the pot. Then they lit a fire under the pot. The fire cooked the stone soup.

The first traveler ate some soup. "M-m-m," he said. "The soup is good now. But green beans and a turnip would make it better."

"You're right! The wolf did not eat all my green beans," said one woman. She ran home and took the beans from under her bed.

"And I have a turnip," said another woman. She ran home and took the turnip from under a basket.

The travelers put the beans and the turnip into the pot.

"M-m-m. Smell the soup! It is better now," said the second traveler. "But peas and beets would make it even better. Can you find some?"

"You're right! It does smell good," said a woman.

"The wolf did not eat all my peas and beets," said one man. "I think I still have some at my house." And he ran to get them.

"Here," he said when he came back. He put the peas and beets into the pot.

"M-m-m. Smell the soup now. It is much better," said the third traveler. "But meat would make it much, much better. That is what the queen has in her soup."

"You ate with the queen?" the people asked in surprise.

Then they took all their food and put it into the pot.

"M-m-m!" said the people.

"M-m-m!" said the travelers. "This is soup fit for a queen!"

"You're wise men to make real soup from stones," said the people.

"Wise men need sleep," said the travelers.

"Take our beds!" said the people.

The three men went to sleep for the night. The next day they went off down the road to the next town.

Reader's Response

Do you think you would like stone soup? Tell why or why not.

SELECTION FOLLOW-UP

STONE SOUP

Questions

1. What two things did the travelers need when they came to the town?
2. How did the travelers get food from the people to make stone soup?
3. How did the travelers make stone soup? Name the steps.
4. Do you think the travelers were wise men? Tell why you think so.

Writing to Learn

THINK AND DECIDE Draw a soup pot.

WRITE Draw what you would put in your pot. Write your own soup recipe.

Songs About Stories

Sometimes stories are told through music. People with stories to tell sometimes write music to go with the words.

Raffi is a man who sings stories for children all over the world. He sometimes uses rhymes we all know, as in "Baa Baa Black Sheep." Other times he makes up new songs to tell a story. He did this for "Baby Beluga."

▲ This is the beluga whale in one of Raffi's songs.

Raffi is singing a story song. ▲

Ella Jenkins sings stories, too. In some of her songs, she sings a rhyme over and over again. It's fun to clap along with her story songs.

Singing a story helps you remember it in a special way.

▼ Ella Jenkins makes story songs fun.

Alanike and the *Storyteller*

written by Donita Creola
illustrated by Jerry Pinkney

Sometimes a boy or a girl in a story may be just like you.

Alanike was a little girl who lived in a small village in Africa. She went to the village school every day. She worked hard. She wanted to know everything about everything. Sometimes Alanike worked so hard there was no time to play with the other boys and girls.

One day Alanike came home from school looking tired.

Alanike's grandfather hugged her. "Cheer up, Alanike," he said. "Listen. Do you hear the talking drums? They are saying that the storyteller will tell stories this very night. We will go and listen to him. His stories will cheer you up."

After dinner Alanike and her grandfather took the long path to the storyteller's house. They could hear the drums calling the people in from their work and play.

The storyteller told his stories as he had heard them when he was a boy. His stories were about people who lived in Alanike's village long ago.

There were stories about times when there was not enough rain. There were stories about times when there was a lot of food and dancing.

The story Alanike liked best was about a little boy named Bola. Bola had lived in her village long ago. He had worked so hard in school that he had no friends. He didn't have time to play or to have fun. Alanike thought that she knew a little girl just like Bola. Alanike listened to every word. She did not want the story to end.

The stories were over too soon. She walked back to her house hand in hand with her grandfather.

"Alanike," said her grandfather, "you are smiling now. Tell me what the storyteller said to bring back your smile."

"Oh, Grandfather," said Alanike. "The storyteller told me not to work so hard that I forget to save time for my friends."

From that day on Alanike still worked hard. She still wanted to learn everything about everything. But she always saved time for her friends.

Reader's Response

Alanike learned something from a story. Did you learn something about yourself from this story? What did you learn?

SELECTION FOLLOW-UP

Alanike and the Storyteller

Questions

1. Why didn't Alanike have time to play? How do you know this?
2. Why did Alanike's grandfather think that a story would cheer her up?
3. Do you think Alanike will go to hear the storyteller again? Tell why or why not.
4. Would you like to have Alanike as a friend? Tell why or why not.

Writing to Learn

THINK AND RECALL Pretend you are a storyteller.

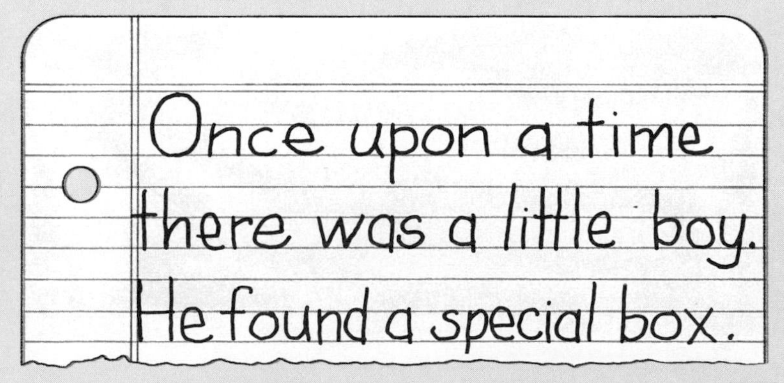

WRITE Write a story you would tell.

Lee Bennett Hopkins
INTERVIEWS

Jerry Pinkney

This is Jerry Pinkney. He draws pictures of many things. He draws pictures for books. He draws pictures for stamps too.

These two stamps show pictures of famous Americans. One stamp shows Harriet Tubman. The other stamp shows Dr. Martin Luther King, Jr.

"My first love is drawing pictures for books," says Pinkney. "I hope that my pictures will help others want to read and look at books."

LAFAYETTE THEATRE
RIVER NIGER
proudly salute the
National Park Service
U.S. Department of the Interior
NIGERIA

"As a child I drew everything," he said. "In school I drew and drew. My drawings made me feel special. I never thought I would grow up one day to be an artist. My mother always told me that I could be anything I wanted to be."

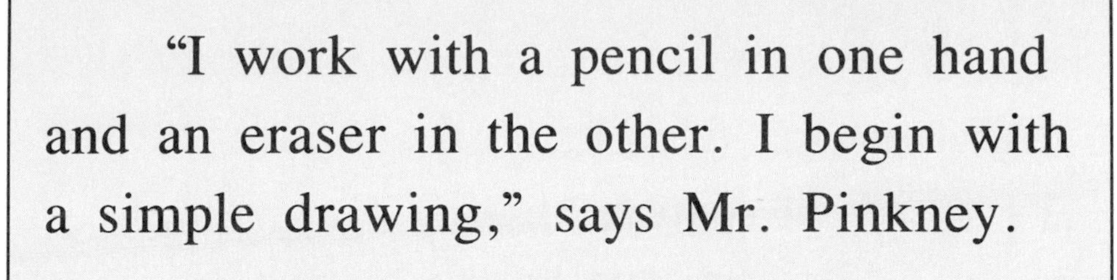

“I work with a pencil in one hand and an eraser in the other. I begin with a simple drawing,” says Mr. Pinkney.

“If I don’t like something that I draw, I erase it. Then I do it all over again. I work on it until I am happy with the drawing.”

You saw some of Mr. Pinkney's drawings in "Alanike and the Storyteller." You can also look in the library for books with Mr. Pinkney's pictures:

The Patchwork Quilt
by Valerie Flourney
Wild Wild Sunflower Child Anna
by Nancy White Carlstrom

Reader's Response

If you met Jerry Pinkney, what would you ask him about his work?

Selection Follow-Up

LEE BENNETT HOPKINS INTERVIEWS

Jerry Pinkney

Questions

1. Why does Mr. Pinkney enjoy drawing?
2. Mr. Pinkney wants his pictures to be just right. How do you know this?
3. Would you like to see some of Jerry Pinkney's books? Tell why or why not.

Writing to Learn

Think and Choose Jerry Pinkney draws pictures for stamps. Draw an outline of a stamp. Show your favorite person on your stamp.

Write Tell who is on your stamp. Write a sentence about your stamp.

Here is a story about two people who had three wishes!

The Three Wishes

by Verna Aardema

Fritz and Anna lived on a farm. It was a small farm. It was also very dry, and things did not grow well. So Fritz and his wife, Anna, were poor.

One day there was a tap, tap, tap on the door. A woman had come to the farm. She had been walking most of the day, and she was hungry. She asked Fritz and Anna to give her something to eat. Fritz and Anna had a pot of soup. They let the woman come in to eat.

"Thank you," said the woman. "You have been most kind. I will grant you three wishes. Remember to use your wishes wisely. Each wish you make will come true."

"Thank you," said Fritz.

"Thank you very much," said Anna.

The woman left.

As soon as the woman was outside the door, Anna said, "Three wishes! Oh, Fritz, I've never been so happy! We can have anything we want!"

Fritz said, "Let's have one wish for you, and one wish for me. Then we will have one wish left for the two of us together."

"I like that," said Anna. "It will be fun to have one wish that is all mine."

For most of the day, Fritz and Anna talked about the three wishes they would make. They talked long after it was time to eat again, and they forgot to cook. They began to get hungry.

By the time Anna and Fritz made soup, they were both very, very hungry. As they sat down to eat, Fritz said, "I wish we had a sausage to go with this soup."

And there on the table was a great big brown sausage!

"Oh, Fritz," said Anna, "there goes your wish! And we have only ONE sausage! I wish we had many, many sausages."

There was Anna's only wish!

PUM, PUM, PUM! Great big sausages rained down on them. They both ducked and tried to get the sausages off them.

"Enough! Enough!" cried Anna. "Get the sausages off me!"

"I can't help you," said Fritz. "I can't get the sausages off me!"

PUM, PUM, PUM, came the sausages. Soon the sausages were all around them.

"What can we do?" asked Anna, from under the sausages.

From under the sausages, Fritz said, "Let's eat them."

"Don't talk that way," said Anna. "This is not funny! I've had enough sausages. What can we do to get out of this?"

"Well," said Fritz, "your wish is gone, and mine is gone. But together we have one wish left. Let's WISH to get out from under the sausages."

Then they both said, "We wish the sausages would go away."

Just as they had come, the sausages went away. There were no sausages anywhere! The big sausage was also gone from the table.

Fritz and Anna were at the table, with only the soup to eat.

"Oh, Fritz," said Anna, "I am so sad! Here we are without any more wishes."

"Anna," said Fritz, "we were happy before the woman came. We can be happy again. Most of all, I wish we had a sausage to eat with this soup."

"Oh, Fritz," said Anna, "I don't want to SEE a sausage for a long time!"

◆ LIBRARY LINK ◆

If you liked this story by Verna Aardema, look for her book Why Mosquitoes Buzz in People's Ears.

Reader's Response

If you had three wishes, would you use them in the same way Fritz and Anna did? How would your wishes be different?

SELECTION FOLLOW-UP

The Three Wishes

Questions

1. How did Fritz and Anna use up their three wishes?
2. If Fritz and Anna had three more wishes, what might they wish for? What makes you think this?
3. Why do you think the woman told them to use their wishes wisely?

Writing to Learn

THINK AND PLAN In this story, Fritz and Anna used up their wishes. Think about what could have happened.

1.	They could have wished for bread.
2.	They could have wished for more wishes.
3.	They could have not used the wishes.

WRITE Use one of the ideas on this page or your own ideas to make up a new ending for the story.

Vocabulary:

Opposites

Words like happy and sad are called opposites. Happy is the opposite of sad. Sad is the opposite of happy.

One night, Anna had a dream. Here is what she saw in her dream. Look for things that are opposite.

Using What You Have Learned

Look at the picture. Think of opposites.

1. The chair is small.

It should be ______.

2. The bird is down.

It should be ______.

3. The sugar is off the table.

It should be ______ the table.

Tell about other things in Anna's dream. Use opposites.

All of Our Noses Are Here

retold by Alvin Schwartz
illustrated by Karen Ann Weinhaus

Mr. Brown has a problem.
Someone is missing.

The Browns went out to row in their boat. When the sun began to go down, they rowed back to the dock.

"Everyone line up," said Mr. Brown. "Let us see if anyone fell out of the boat.

"One is here.
Two are here.
Three are here.
And four are here."

"But we are five," said Mrs. Brown.

"I think I counted wrong," said Mr. Brown. "I will count again.

One is here.
Two are here.
Three are here.
And four are here."

"Only four?" asked Mrs. Brown.

"Yes," said Mr. Brown. "One of us is missing."

Mrs. Brown began to cry. So did the others.

"Why are all of you crying?" a fisherman asked.

"Five of us went rowing," said Mr. Brown. "But only four came back."

"Are you sure?" the fisherman asked.

Mr. Brown counted again.
Again he counted only four.

"I know what is wrong," said the fisherman. "You forgot to count yourself."

"I will try again," said Mr. Brown. "I will count myself first.

One is here.
Two are here.
Three are here.
And four are here.
And five are here.
And SIX are here!"

"But there should be five," said Mrs. Brown.

"No," said Mr. Brown. "Now we are six."

"But I do not see another person," said Mrs. Brown.

They looked in the boat and under the dock. They looked behind the trees and in the grass, but they did not find anyone.

"Come out! Come out! Whoever you are!" Mr. Brown called.

The others called too, but no one came out.

When the fisherman heard the calling, he went to see what was wrong.

"Now there are six of us, not five," said Mr. Brown. "But we cannot find this extra person."

"Are you sure there are six?" the fisherman asked.

Mr. Brown counted again, and again he counted six.

"You are doing it all wrong," said the fisherman. "You counted yourself twice. Let me show you the right way to count."

The fisherman said, "Everybody, get down on your hands and knees. Now stick your noses into the mud and pull them out."

"Now count the holes your noses made," said the fisherman.

Mr. Brown counted.

"One is here.
Two are here.
Three are here.
Four are here.
And FIVE are here."

"All of our noses are here!" Mr. Brown said. "Now we can go home."

◆ LIBRARY LINK ◆

"All of Our Noses Are Here" came from a book called All of Our Noses Are Here and Other Noodle Tales. *Look for it in your library.*

Reader's Response

Do you think the fisherman's way of counting noses was good? Tell why or why not.

Selection Follow-Up

All of Our Noses Are Here

Questions

1. Why did Mr. Brown count noses?
2. Mrs. Brown cried when Mr. Brown only counted *four* people. Why do you think she cried?
3. What happened when Mr. Brown counted noses?
4. Name one thing that tells you that this story is make-believe.

Writing to Learn

Think and Invent Mr. Brown needs to learn how to count. How would you teach him?

Write One way to teach him is with a counting book. Make a counting book.

The Midnight Farm

written by Reeve Lindbergh
illustrated by Susan Jeffers

The farm can hold many surprises in the middle of the night.

Here is the dark when day is done,
Here is the dark with no moon or sun,
Here is the dark when all lights are out,
Here is the heart of the dark.

Here is the dark of the chair in the hall
Where one old dog curls up in a ball,
Breathing each breath with a rise and a fall
In the dark of the chair in the hall.

Here is the dark by the big wood stove
Where two white cats have a leftover glove
And a birthday card that was signed with love
In the dark by the big wood stove.

Here is the dark of the maple tree
Where a raccoon family, one, two, three,

Is making a home in a place that was free
In the dark of the maple tree.

Here is the dark by the barnyard gate
Where four farm geese are staying up late.

They know wild geese will come if they wait
In the dark by the barnyard gate.

Here is the dark of the stable door
Where five horses stamp their feet on the floor

And blow through their noses and stamp some more
In the dark of the stable door.

Here is the dark of the midnight farm,
Safe and still and full and warm,

Deep in the dark and free from harm
In the dark of the midnight farm.

Reader's Response

Which part of the poem did you think was the prettiest? Tell why.

Writing a Story

You have just read stories that have been told to people all over the world for many years. Think of a story that you have heard or read. How can you share that story with someone else? One way to share it is to write it down on paper.

Getting Ready

All stories have a beginning, a middle, and an end. Look at the box below, and think about the questions to help you plan your story.

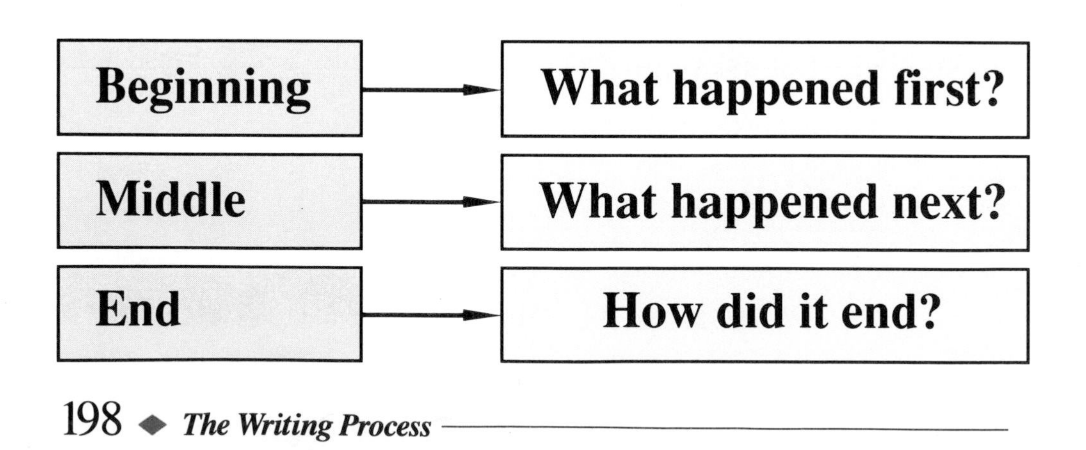

Writing

Use the notes in your box to write the story you would like to share. Write what happened first. Write what happened next. End your story with what happened last.

Listening to My Writing

Read your story to a partner. Does your partner know what happened? Tell things more clearly if you need to.

Sharing

Everyone's stories can go into a class book. Call your book *Stories We Know*.

Making up a New Ending

The stories in this unit have been told over and over. When people retell a story, they sometimes change it. You and someone else in your class will now make up a new ending for a story in this unit.

Remember to:

- Take turns giving ideas.
- Listen when the other person talks.

First, think of the stories in this unit. Decide together what story you will pick. With your partner think of some new endings for the story. Talk about them. Decide on one new ending for the story. Take turns telling the story with its new ending.

Why the Sun and the Moon Live in the Sky by Elphinstone Dayrell *(Houghton Mifflin, 1969)*. This African folktale tells how the moon and sun came to live in the sky.

Morris Tells Boris Mother Moose Stories and Rhymes by Bernard Wiseman *(Dodd, Mead, 1979)*. Boris the Bear can't sleep, so Morris the Moose tells him funny Mother Moose rhymes and stories.

Red Riding Hood retold by James Marshall *(Dial Books, 1987)*. A little girl visits her sick grandmother and meets a stranger.

Browsing for Books

A Place to Read

Do you ever " curl up with a good book "? It is something almost everyone does from time to time. When you are tired, a book can be your very best friend.

Many people have special places where they go to read their books, or just to look at the pictures in them. Do you? Beds are *wonderful* places to read when it's cold and you want to stay cozy and warm. The soft grass under a shady tree can be a fine place to stay cool with a good book. You can also keep a book in the car for the times when there's nothing to look at out the window. Sometimes it's nice to snuggle up to someone older who can read a book *to* you.

The most important thing is not where you read, but that you read something every day. Books can be your friends for life.

FULL-LENGTH BOOK

Dreams

READING TEACHER: CHILDREN'S CHOICE 1974

EZRA JACK KEATS

It was hot.
After supper Roberto came
to his window to talk with Amy.
"Look what I made in school today—
a paper mouse!"

"Does it do anything?" Amy asked.

Roberto thought for a while.
"I don't know," he said. Then he put
the mouse on the window sill.

As it grew darker, the city got quieter.
"Bedtime, Roberto," called his mother.
"Bedtime for you, too,"
other mothers called.
"Good-night, Amy."
"Good-night, Roberto."
"G-o-o-o-d-night!" echoed the parrot.
Soon they were all in bed.

Someone began to dream.

Soon everybody was dreaming—
except one person.

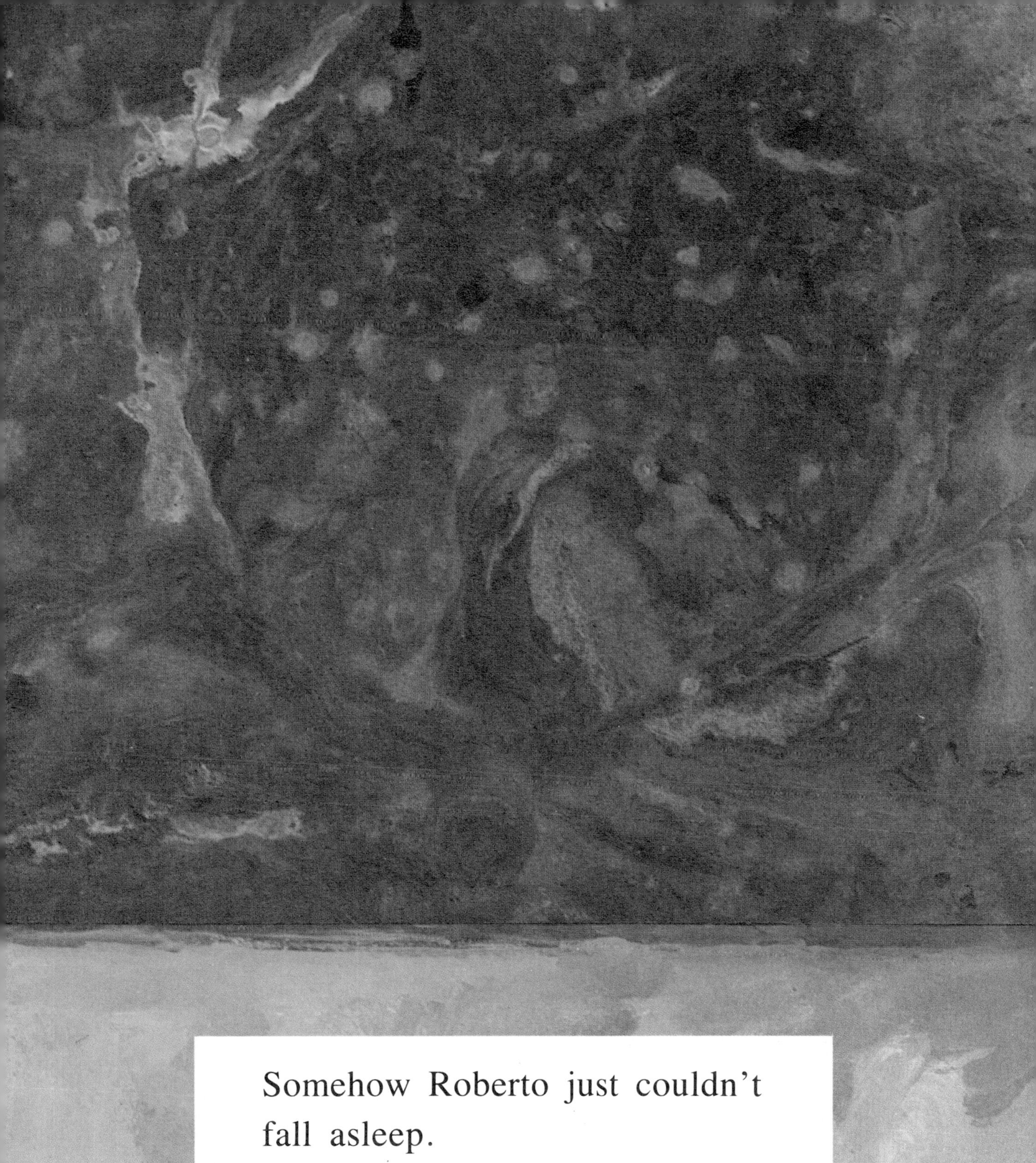

Somehow Roberto just couldn't fall asleep.
It got later and later.

Finally he got up
and went to the window.
What he saw down in the street
made him gasp!

There was Archie's cat!
A big dog had chased him into a box.
The dog snarled.
"He's trapped!" thought Roberto.
"What should I do?"

Then it happened!
His pajama sleeve
brushed the paper mouse
off the window sill.
It sailed away from him.

Down it fell,
turning this way
and that,
casting a big shadow
on the wall.

The shadow grew bigger–
and bigger–

and BIGGER!
The dog howled and ran away.

The cat dashed across the street
and jumped through Archie's open window.
"Wow! Wait till I tell Archie
what happened!"
thought Roberto.
"That was some mouse!"
He yawned and went back to bed.

Morning came and everybody was getting up.
Except one person.

Roberto was fast asleep, dreaming.

A

afternoon We play every afternoon before we eat supper.

ago My mother was born a long time ago.

alone Mark sat alone in the new class.

also Cats like to eat fish. They also like milk.

Americans The people who live in the United States are Americans.

another Carol picked out a book. Then she started to look for another one.

anyone That dog will come to anyone.

anywhere Sara does not go anywhere without asking her mother.

artist The artist has made many paintings.

Americans

artist

B

baked My mother baked bread in the oven.

baked

barn In winter, the cows live inside the barn.

barn

basket My dog likes to sleep in his basket.

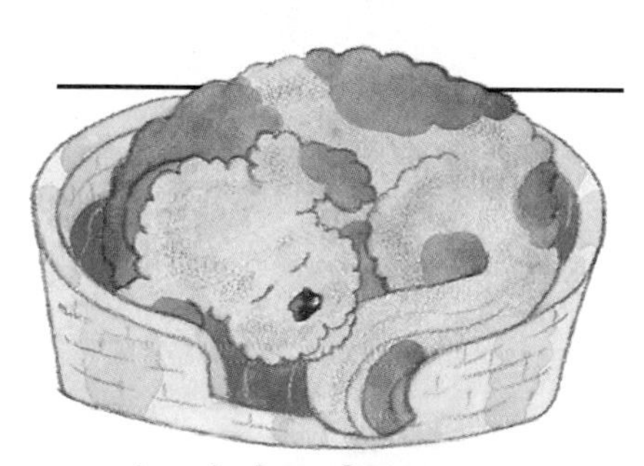
my dog's **basket**

beautiful Everyone comes to look at this place because it is so beautiful.

because It is wet outside because it just rained.

been We went to the lake. Have you been there?

before I brush my teeth beforc I go to bed.

began Jake began to paint the wall.

Jake **began** to paint.

begin We will begin to eat in five minutes.

behind Jan finished the race behind the winner.

better I liked this book better than that one.

boat

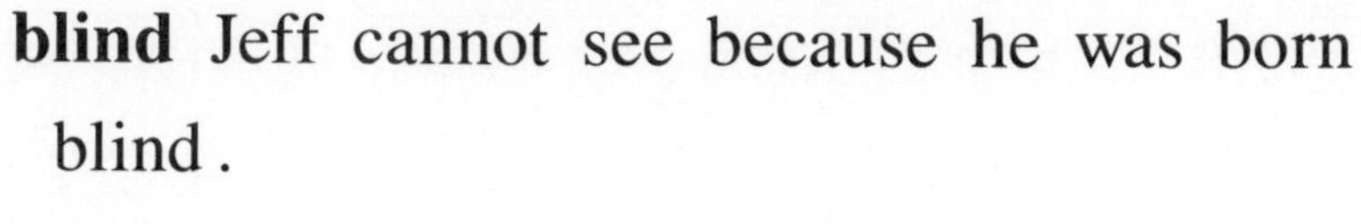

blind Jeff cannot see because he was born blind.

boat Sam likes to fish from a boat on the river.

boy Pete is the new boy in our class.

bread We make toast from bread.

castle

C

cart It's easy to move things around in a cart.

castle The king lived in a castle.

chair The cat is sitting on the chair.

child Daniel is still a child. He is six years old.

We are **coming.**

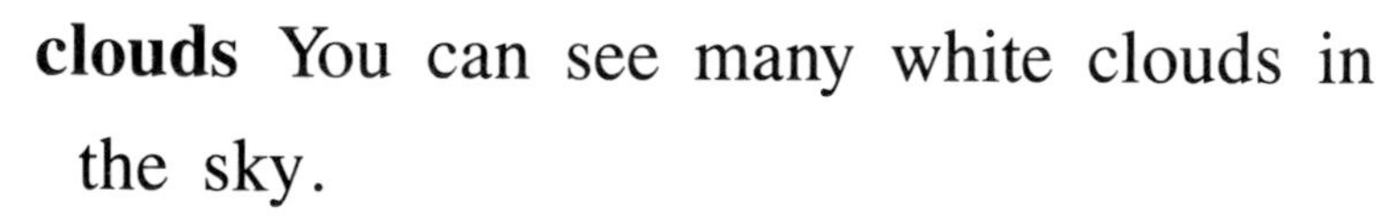

clouds You can see many white clouds in the sky.

cold Tom has a red nose because he is sick with a cold.

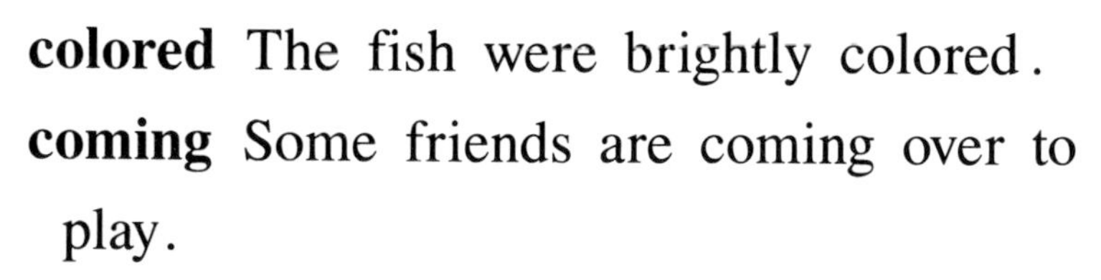

colored The fish were brightly colored.

coming Some friends are coming over to play.

Dad **cooked** dinner.

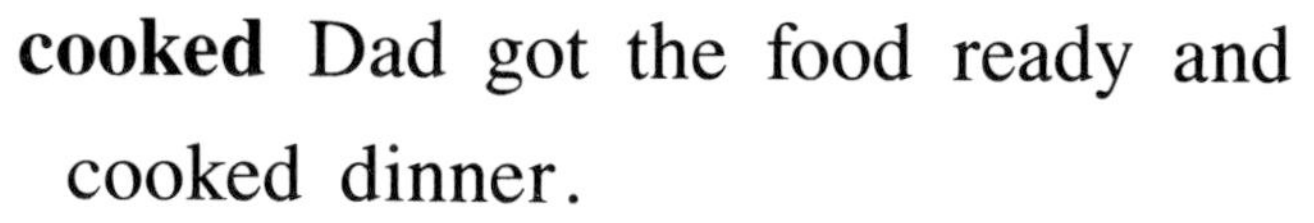

cooked Dad got the food ready and cooked dinner.

count Can you count the numbers from one to twenty?

country Rachel lives on a farm in the country.

cousin Dan is my uncle. His son, Rob, is my cousin.

cried Alex cried when his best friend moved away.

country

D

dancing Pat likes dancing to fast music.

dear The letter said, "Dear Pete, We miss you."

dinner Dinner is the biggest meal of the day.

does My big sister does homework every night.

drank Steve drank a glass of milk.

drew Roz drew this picture with a pen last night.

drums Rick likes to beat on the drums.

ducklings The ducklings all stayed near the mother duck.

dancing

drums

ducklings

eggs

erase

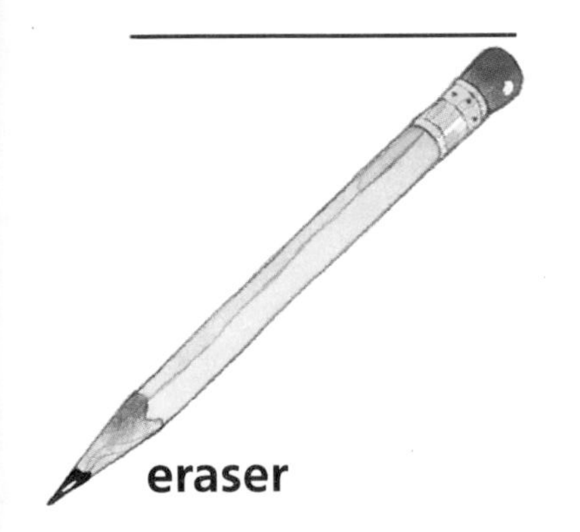
eraser

family

E

eggs The hen lays fresh eggs every day.

enough That was a big dinner. I had enough to eat.

erase If you make a mistake, erase it.

eraser This pencil has an eraser to rub out mistakes.

even We will have our picnic even if it rains.

ever Have you ever been to the circus?

every The street was empty, and every shop was closed.

everything Everything Deb wears is pink.

everywhere John lost his ball. He looked everywhere for it.

extra There are six apples for five people. There is one extra apple.

F

family My father, my mother, and I are the only three people in my family.

famous Our shop is famous because so many people know about it.

far It takes a long time to walk to the park bccause it is far away.

felt Ann felt the cat's soft fur.

fingers Grandma wears many rings on her fingers.

fisherman That fisherman has lots of fish.

forget Don't forget to feed the fish.

forgot Sara forgot to tie her shoes.

four There are two boys and two girls on the grass. Altogether there are four children.

funny Everyone smiled when Fred told a funny joke.

Ann **felt** the fur.

four children

G

garden Corn, lettuce, and tomatoes grow in my garden.

girl The little girl was drawing.

garden

girl

There **goes** the bus.

goes Helen was running for the bus, but missed it. "There goes the bus," she said.

golden The setting sun gave everything a golden color.

goodbye As she left, Nancy kissed her grandpa goodbye.

goodness When Grace saw a green man in her garden, she said, "Goodness, what a surprise!"

grandfather

grandfather My grandfather, my mother's father, has lots of grandchildren.

great We have a great number of books in our house.

guitar

guitar It is nice to sing as you play the guitar.

H

head

happily Juan and Hernando arc smiling because they are playing so happily.

head Everyone has a head.

hello Sam and James said "hello" when they met.

horse My sister likes to ride her horse.

hugged Her mother held Meg close and hugged her.

hungry Because Rick did not eat any breakfast, he was very hungry by lunchtime.

horse

hugged

I

I'm Sean said to himself, "Today, I'm six years old!"

island We had to travel to the island by boat.

island

K

king The king lived in a big castle.

knees When I wear shorts, my knees show.

knew Tony knew the names of all his classmates.

king

lemonade

letter

library

L

learn Bob would like to learn how to play the drums.

lemonade I love to drink lemonade on a hot day.

let's Let's go to the park and play!

letter Tim wrote his friend a letter.

library You can get books from the library.

listen Fred likes to listen to music.

lived Benita lived in the city.

lose Did Sally lose her pencil? Yes, she forgot where she put it.

M

most We have been painting this room for days, and most of it is done now.

move Greg's books were all over the table. The teacher asked him to move them.

moved Grandma used to live near us, but she moved away.

moving Tom was moving to the new house across the street.

must Dan must be on time for class.

myself The little girl said, "I baked the cake all by myself, without any help."

moving

N

never Before he went to the beach, Matt had never seen the sea.

news Dad reads the newspaper to find out the news.

nothing The cat licked the plate so nothing was left on it.

I baked it **myself.**

Dad reads the **news.**

O

once Many years ago, Rob once saw a live snake.

only It was so hot that Bert was wearing only shorts.

or Do you want to eat carrots or beans?

own Jill was given her own lunch box.

painted

pictures

pretend

queen and **princess**

P

painted Lee painted a blue and green house.

paper Fran wrote a letter on white paper.

pencil I like to draw with a pencil.

pictures Jim has pictures hanging on his walls.

pocketbook My mother always has her pocketbook with her.

poor This poor cat has hurt its paw.

pretend Dan likes to pretend he is a king.

princess The queen's baby girl is a princess.

Q

quack The ducks all said, "Quack, quack."

queens The two queens lived in a castle.

R

remember Can you remember when you were two years old?

road The car drove along the road.

row Scott can row a boat.

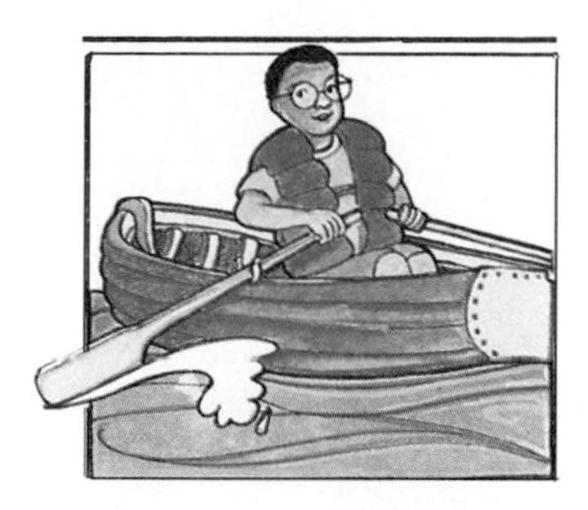

row

S

sausage I ate a sausage with my pancakes.

says The dentist says that my teeth are fine.

second Beth was first in the race, and Mark was second.

share I share my pillow with my doll.

should You should eat three meals a day.

silly Gary was wearing a silly purple and green hat.

simple Megan likes to make simple clothes.

slipped The bear slipped on the ice and almost fell down.

smiles Lee smiles when he is happy.

I **share** my pillow.

making **simple** clothes

slipped

stopped

storyteller

summer

surprises

soft The pillow feels very soft.

sometimes Rosanne sometimes wears her hair in a bow.

sorry Pete was sorry that he had broken the dish.

soup I like to drink soup out of a cup.

special Tim wore his special shirt to the party.

stamps This letter needs more stamps.

stood When he saw the snake, Brad stood very still.

stopped The car stopped at the light.

storyteller The storyteller told them many great stories.

straight This stick is crooked, but that one is straight.

summer It is warm in summer. We wear shorts every day.

surprises I had two surprises today. Two frogs jumped out of my bag.

T

table We set the table for dinner.

tadpoles We catch tadpoles to watch them turn into frogs.

tadpoles

talked Everyone talked and shouted at the same time.

teach The teacher will teach us many things.

teach

tears John had tears in his eyes as he said goodbye.

tents When my family went camping, we stayed in three tents.

tents

third Tad won the race. Matt was second, and Jed came in third.

through The dog walked through the open door.

thumb You have one thumb on each hand.

tiny An ant is a tiny animal.

town A town has many houses in it.

toy The dog likes to play with his toy.

the dog's **toy**

traveler Ann is a real traveler. She has visited many places.

tries Susan tries to make cakes. They usually taste great!

try Bob will try to win the race.

The top **turned.**

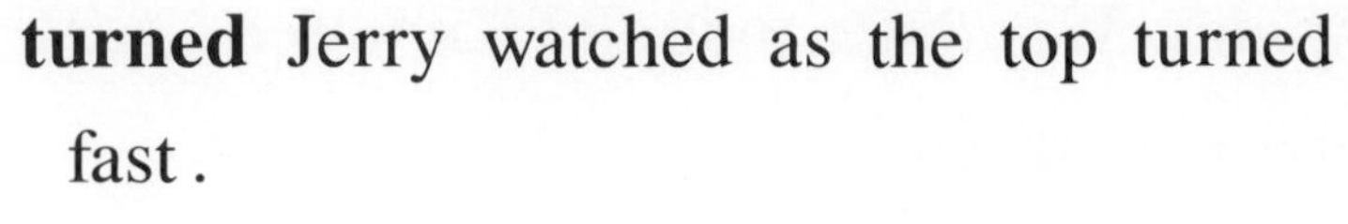

turned Jerry watched as the top turned fast.

turnip You can buy a turnip in a vegetable shop.

twice Fred was at bat two times. He hit the ball twice.

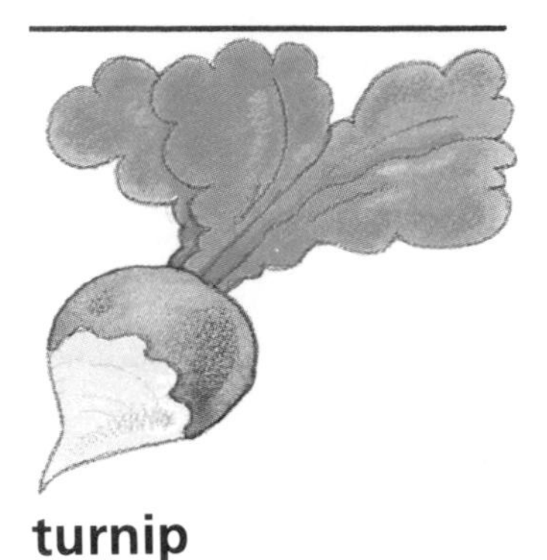

turnip

U

upon I like "Once upon a time" stories.

used Meg used a broom to sweep up the leaves.

village

V

village Helen lives in a village with only nine houses.

visit Lee goes to visit her grandparents every week.

Lee goes to **visit.**

W

wear Beth likes to wear her red dress.

whistles The man uses whistles to call his dogs.

white New snow is white.

whoever Whoever wins the race will win the prize.

wife Mr. Rodrigo lives with his wife, Mrs. Rodrigo.

wisely John is careful with his money and spends it wisely.

woman The little girl wants to grow up and become a woman.

woods Many kinds of trees grow in the woods.

words There are many words in this book.

write Joe likes to write letters to his friends.

wrote Joe wrote four letters yesterday.

yourself Do you ever talk to yourself?

girl and **woman**

woods

This book has **words.**

write

The following story critical words appear in *A New Day.* The words are listed next to the number of the page on which they first appear.

Unit 1

Your Friend, Little Bear

11 summer
goodbye
baked
lemonade

12 drank
talked

17 learn
write

Alone

24 alone

25 does

26 island

27 everything

31 sorry

33 felt
because

A New Day in the City

44 I'm

46 surprises
paper
painted
family

47 pictures

48 afternoon

Together

53 blind
words

54 try

55 fingers
special

56 own

58 share

Goldfish and Lee

67 visit
teach
horse

68 before
says

69 smiles

70 tries

71 soft

We Are Best Friends

79 news

81 moved

83 letter

85 boy

88 tadpoles

Unit 2

Once Upon a Time

110 begin
once
upon
beautiful

111 pretend

113 castle

114 happily
ever

The Man, the Cat, and the Sky

120 country
listen
colored

121 king

124 town

127 tents

Stone Soup

131 traveler
second
third
road

136 cooked
better

Alanike and the Storyteller

145 girl
lived
village

146 grandfather
drums

149 dancing

Lee Bennett Hopkins Interviews Jerry Pinkney

154 stamps

156 drew
artist

157 pencil
eraser
erase

The Three Wishes

160 wife
hungry

161 wisely

162 let's

163 sausage
table

164 only

All of Our Noses Are Here

173 row
count
four

175 fisherman

176 yourself
myself

179 extra

About the Authors

These authors have written some of the stories in this book.

Verna Aardema

Verna Aardema

Verna Aardema began writing books because her little girl liked to listen to a story while she was eating. She made up the stories she told her daughter. Some books that Verna Aardema writes take place in different lands. Before writing one of these books, she reads other books about the country where the story takes place. *(Born 1911)*

ALIKI

Aliki's full name is Aliki Liacouras Brandenberg. Aliki says, "I write two kinds of books – fiction (which comes from my own ideas) and nonfiction (which I must find out about from others)." She also draws pictures for books. Aliki's husband, Franz Brandenberg, is a writer. She has drawn the pictures for all of her husband's books. *(Born 1929)*

ALIKI

NIKKI GIOVANNI

Nikki Giovanni writes poetry. She says she likes to write for children and to read to children. She says she wants her poetry to touch their hearts and minds. Nikki Giovanni also hopes that adults will like her poetry. *(Born 1943)*

NIKKI GIOVANNI

Ezra Jack Keats

Ezra Jack Keats

Ezra Jack Keats wrote many books. He also illustrated books. He began painting when he was about four years old. He remembered drawing pictures on the kitchen table. His mother was very proud of his drawings. Ezra Jack Keats won many awards for his work. *(1916–1983)*

Arnold Lobel

Arnold Lobel

Arnold Lobel wrote and illustrated books for children. His books have won many awards. He liked to make books for children. One of the things Arnold Lobel liked was being able to change a character that was not acting the way he thought it should act. *(1933–1987)*

JAMES MARSHALL

JAMES MARSHALL

James Marshall writes and illustrates books for children. He also illustrates books for other authors. He has won many awards for his books. James Marshall lives in Massachusetts. He has an English bulldog and seven cats. *(Born 1942)*

ELSE HOLMELUND MINARIK

ELSE HOLMELUND MINARIK

Else Holmelund Minarik began writing when she was a teacher. When she taught first grade, she could not find enough books for her students. She then began to write them herself. Children loved the books she wrote about Little Bear and his family. Now she is writing books about other animals, too. *(Born 1920)*

ANNE ROCKWELL

ANNE ROCKWELL

Anne Rockwell writes books for children. She also illustrates books. She says she has a special place to write her books. It is a "secret writing room for me, with a window that looks up only into the trees. I have been having a wonderful time working in it." *(Born 1934)*

ALVIN SCHWARTZ

ALVIN SCHWARTZ

Alvin Schwartz writes books for children. He likes to write books because he can find out about things. He says, "I write in a small out building which is 8 feet by 8 feet but almost all windows." Several of his books have been selected as American Library Association Notable Books. *(Born 1927)*

AUTHOR INDEX

"The Three Wishes" by Verna Aardema, © 1989 by Silver, Burdett & Ginn Inc.

"Together" by Anne Rockwell, © 1989 by Silver, Burdett & Ginn Inc.

"two friends" from *Spin a Soft Black Song* by Nikki Giovanni. Copyright © 1971 by Nikki Giovanni. Reprinted by permission of Farrar, Straus and Giroux, Inc.

We Are Best Friends written and illustrated by Aliki. Copyright © 1982 by Aliki Brandenburg. Adapted and reprinted by permission of Greenwillow Books (A Division of William Morrow).

"Your Friend, Little Bear" excerpt adapted from *Little Bear's Friend* by Else Holmelund Minarik, pictures by Maurice Sendak. Text copyright © 1960 by Else Holmelund Minarik, illustrations copyright © 1960 by Maurice Sendak. Reprinted by permission of the American publisher, Harper & Row, Publishers, Inc., and of the British publisher William Heinemann Ltd.

COVER: Delana Bettoli
DESIGN: Design Five, NYC and Kirchoff/Wohlberg in cooperation with Silver, Burdett & Ginn

ILLUSTRATION: 4, James Marshall; 5, (t & br) Dorothy Cullinan, (bl) Aliki; 6, (t) Karen Ann Weinhaus, (b) Jean Mou Sien-Tseng; 7, Betsy Hazelton; 10–18, Maurice Sendak; 19, Christa Kieffer; 20–21, Leslie Alfred; 24–34, Arnold Lobel; 35, Susan Jaekel; 36, (t) "Mexican Frog" watercolor by Valeie Ganz from a photo from Ardea Photographic, in *Frogs* edited by Lynn Hughes, published by W.H. Allen & Co., copyright © 1982; (b) from *The Tale of Mr. Jeremy Fisher* by Beatrix Potter, published by Fredrick Warne & Co., 1906, copyright © Frederick Warne & Co., 1906, reproduced by permission of Penguin Books Ltd.; 37, (tl) from *The Wind and the Willows* by Kenneth Grahame, illustrated by Michael Hague, copyright © 1980 by Ariel Inc., reprinted by permission of Henry Holt & Co., Inc.; (tr) Kermit the Frog, copyright © 1982 by Henson Associates, Inc., all rights reserved; (cl & cr) from *Frog on His Own* by Mercer Mayer, copyright © 1973 by Mercer Mayer, reproduced by permission of the publisher, Dial Books for Young Readers; (b) from *We Are Best of Friends* by Aliki, copyright © 1982 by Aliki Brandenburg, reproduced with permission of the publisher, Greenwillow Books, a division of William Morrow & Co., Inc.; 38–48, Dorothy Cullinan; 49, Susan Jaekel; 50–51, Reynold Ruffins; 52–58, Kim Mulkey; 59, Susan Jaekel; 66–75, Howard Post; 78–90, Aliki; 91, Susan Jaekel; 93–103, James Marshall; 94, Bob Filipowich; 111–113, Betsy Hazelton; 115, Betsy Hazelton; 116–117, Clinton Arrowood; 118, Michelle Fridkin; 120–129, Jean Mou Sien-Tseng; 130–140, Steven Schindler; 141, Susan Jaekel; 143, (tl) Paul Turnbaugh; 144–152, Jerry Pinkney; 154, (t) Floyd Cooper, (cl & cr) Jerry Pinkney; 160–167, Andrea Eberbach; 170–171, Michelle Fridkin; 172–184, Karen Ann Weinhaus; 185, Susan Jaekel; 186–197, Susan Jeffers; 203–231, Ezra Jack Keats; 232, Richard Kolding, Tom Sperling; 233, Bob Barner, Cheryl Kirk Noll, Tom Sperling; 234, Richard Kolding, Tom Sperling ; 235, Bob Barner, Richard Kolding, Cheryl Kirk Noll, Tom Sperling; 236, Bob Barner, Richard Kolding, Cheryl Kirk Noll; 237, Bob Barner, Richard Kolding, Cheryl Kirk Noll; 238, Richard Kolding, Tom Sperling; 239, Richard Kolding, Cheryl Kirk Noll, Tom Sperling; 240, Bob Barner, Richard Kolding, Tom Sperling; 241, Richard Kolding, Cheryl Kirk Noll, Tom Sperling; 242, Bob Barner, Richard Kolding, Cheryl Kirk Noll; 243, Bob Barner, Richard Kolding, Cheryl Kirk Noll, Tom Sperling; 244, Richard Kolding, Cheryl Kirk Noll, Tom Sperling; 245, Bob Barner, Richard Kolding; 246, Bob Barner, Cheryl Kirk Noll, Tom Sperling; 247, Bob Barner, Richard Kilding, Cheryl Kirk Noll, Tom Sperling.

PHOTOGRAPHY: 8, Art Resource, New York; 36, (t) Lynn Hughes and Cawdor Studio; 63, (tl) Ken Sherman/Bruce Coleman, (cr) Barbara Van Cleve/Click, Chicago, (bl) Mike Medici; 64, (t) Scott C. Harvey; 77, Lawrence Migdale; 92, © Frank Siteman 1988; 106, (t) reproduced with permission of Atheneum Publishers, an imprint of Macmillan Publishing Company from *May I Bring a Friend?* by Beatrice Schenk de Regniers, illustrated by Beni Montressor, illustrations copyright © 1964 by Beni Montressor, (c) reproduced with permission of Margaret K. McElderry Books, an imprint of Macmillan Publishing Company from *Friends* by Helme Heine, copyright © 1982 by Gertraud Middlehauve Verlag, Koln, (b) reproduced from *My Friend John* by Charlotte Zolotow, pictures by Ben Shecter, copyright © 1968, with permission from the publisher, Harper & Row; 108, courtesy, Dr. Dexter W. Lawson Collection/© Susan Van Etten; 110–114, Richard Haynes; 142, *The Raffi Singable Songbook,* photos by Carlos Vergara; 143, (tr) Richard Howard, (bc) Bernadale Richter from "Ella Jenkins Presents My Street Begins At My House," Folkways Records; 155–157, Victoria Beller-Smith; 158, from *The Patchwork Quilt* by Valerie Flournoy, illustrated by Jerry Pinkney, published in 1985 by Dial Books for Young Readers, from *Wild Wild Sunflower Child Anna* by Nancy White Carlstrom, illustrated by Jerry Pinkney, published in 1987 by Macmillan; 201, from *Why the Sun and the Moon Live in the Sky* by Elphinstone Dayrell, illustrated by Blair Lent, published in 1969 by Houghton Mifflin Company, from *Morris Tells Boris Mother Moose Stories and Rhymes,* written and illustrated by Bernard Wiseman, published in 1979 by Dodd, Mead, and from *Red Riding Hood,* retold and illustrated by James Marshall, published in 1987 by Dial Books for Young Readers; 251, (b) H.W. Wilson Company; 252, (t) David Des Jardines; 253, (t) H.W. Wilson Company, (b) Harper Junior Books; 254, (t) H.W. Wilson Company.

G H I J–VHP–96 95 94 93 92 91 90 89